RIHANNA

WISE PUBLICATIONS
PART OF THE MUSIC SALES GROUP
LONDON / NEW YORK / PARIS / SYDNEY / COPENHAGEN / BERLIN / MADRID / HONG KONG / TOKYO

ALSO AVAILABLE IN THE REALLY EASY PIANO SERIES...

ABBA
25 GREAT HITS. ORDER NO. AM980430

CHILDREN'S FAVOURITES
20 POPULAR HITS. ORDER NO. AM998745

CHRISTMAS
24 FESTIVE CHART HITS. ORDER NO. AM980496

CLASSICAL FAVOURITES
24 WELL-KNOWN FAVOURITES. ORDER NO. AM993366

COLDPLAY
20 SONGS FROM COLDPLAY. ORDER NO. AM989593

ELTON JOHN
24 CLASSIC SONGS. ORDER NO. AM987844

FRANK SINATRA
21 CLASSIC SONGS. ORDER NO. AM987833

GREAT FILM SONGS
22 BIG FILM HITS. ORDER NO. AM993344

GREAT SHOWSTOPPERS
20 POPULAR STAGE SONGS. ORDER NO. AM993355

JAZZ GREATS
22 JAZZ FAVOURITES. ORDER NO. AM1000857

LOVE SONGS
22 CLASSIC LOVE SONGS. ORDER NO. AM989582

MICHAEL JACKSON
19 CLASSIC HITS. ORDER NO. AM1000604

MORE 21ST CENTURY HITS
21 POPULAR HITS. ORDER NO. AM996534

MOZART
22 CLASSICAL FAVOURITES. ORDER NO. AM1000648

NEW CHART HITS
19 BIG CHART HITS. ORDER NO. AM996523

NO. 1 HITS
22 POPULAR CLASSICS. ORDER NO. AM993388

POP HITS
22 GREAT SONGS. ORDER NO. AM980408

SHOWSTOPPERS
24 STAGE HITS. ORDER NO. AM982784

TV HITS
25 POPULAR HITS. ORDER NO. AM985435

60S HITS
25 CLASSIC HITS. ORDER NO. AM985402

70S HITS
25 CLASSIC SONGS. ORDER NO. AM985413

80S HITS
25 POPULAR HITS. ORDER NO. AM985424

90S HITS
24 POPULAR HITS. ORDER NO. AM987811

50 FABULOUS SONGS
FROM POP SONGS TO CLASSICAL THEMES. ORDER NO. AM999449

50 GREAT SONGS
FROM POP SONGS TO CLASSICAL THEMES. ORDER NO. AM995643

50 HIT SONGS
FROM POP HITS TO JAZZ CLASSICS. ORDER NO. AM1000615

PIANO TUTOR
FROM FIRST STEPS TO PLAYING IN A WIDE
RANGE OF STYLES — FAST!. ORDER NO. AM996303

ALL TITLES CONTAIN BACKGROUND NOTES FOR EACH SONG PLUS
PLAYING TIPS AND HINTS.

PUBLISHED BY
WISE PUBLICATIONS
14-15 BERNERS STREET, LONDON, W1T 3LJ, UK.

EXCLUSIVE DISTRIBUTORS:
MUSIC SALES LIMITED
DISTRIBUTION CENTRE, NEWMARKET ROAD, BURY ST EDMUNDS,
SUFFOLK, IP33 3YB, UK.
MUSIC SALES PTY LIMITED
UNITS 3-4, 17 WILLFOX STREET, CONDELL PARK
NSW 2200, AUSTRALIA.

ORDER NO. AM1006621
ISBN 978-1-78305-124-3
THIS BOOK © COPYRIGHT 2013 BY WISE PUBLICATIONS,
A DIVISION OF MUSIC SALES LIMITED.

MUSIC ARRANGED BY FIONA BOLTON.
EDITED BY JENNI NOREY.
PRINTED IN THE EU.

YOUR GUARANTEE OF QUALITY
AS PUBLISHERS, WE STRIVE TO PRODUCE EVERY BOOK TO THE HIGHEST
COMMERCIAL STANDARDS. THE MUSIC HAS BEEN FRESHLY ENGRAVED AND
THE BOOK HAS BEEN CAREFULLY DESIGNED TO MINIMISE AWKWARD PAGE
TURNS AND TO MAKE PLAYING FROM IT A REAL PLEASURE.
PARTICULAR CARE HAS BEEN GIVEN TO SPECIFYING ACID-FREE, NEUTRAL-
SIZED PAPER MADE FROM PULPS WHICH HAVE NOT BEEN ELEMENTAL
CHLORINE BLEACHED. THIS PULP IS FROM FARMED SUSTAINABLE FORESTS
AND WAS PRODUCED WITH SPECIAL REGARD FOR THE ENVIRONMENT.
THROUGHOUT, THE PRINTING AND BINDING HAVE BEEN PLANNED TO
ENSURE A STURDY, ATTRACTIVE PUBLICATION WHICH SHOULD GIVE YEARS
OF ENJOYMENT. IF YOUR COPY FAILS TO MEET OUR HIGH STANDARDS,
PLEASE INFORM US AND WE WILL GLADLY REPLACE IT.

WWW.MUSICSALES.COM

Cheers (Drink To That)

Words & Music by Avril Lavigne, Lauren Christy, Graham Edwards, David Alspach, Jermaine Jackson, Robyn Fenty, Andrew Harr, Corey Gibson, Laura Pergolizzi & Stacy Barthe

Sampling Avril Lavigne's 'I'm With You', this party anthem was written to convey a message of overcoming negativity and trying to enjoy your life in the face of adversity. The seventh and final single from Rihanna's fifth studio album, *Loud*, the song reached the top ten in four countries including the USA and Australia.

Hints & Tips: Whenever the right hand has repeated quavers and semiquavers, play these slightly staccato so they don't sound too heavy.

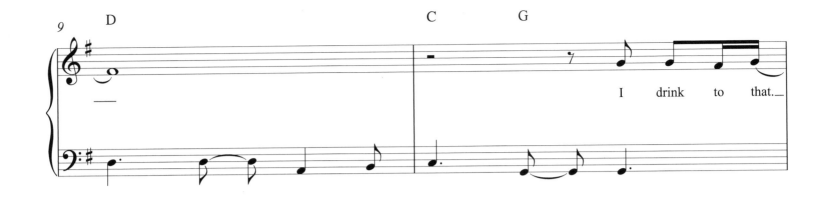

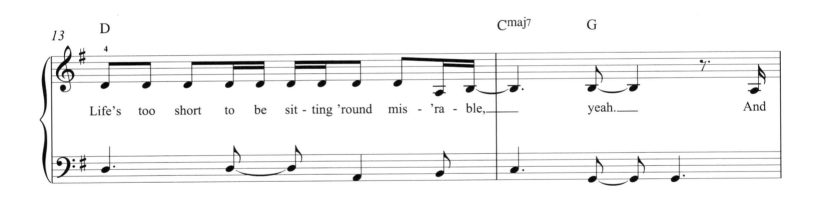

California King Bed

Words & Music by Jermaine Jackson, Priscilla Hamilton, Andrew Harr & Alexander Delicata

This song was a major international hit for RiRi in 2011, claiming the No. 1 spot in Poland and Slovakia and entering the top five in Australia, Brazil, Germany, Austria and New Zealand. With its dynamic contrast between a distorted guitar driven chorus and more delicate acoustic lead verse, the song is a classic example of an American rock hit.

Hints & Tips: The left hand has a lot of stretches in the first half. Roll the wrist from the bottom note to the top if you can't quite reach.

Disturbia

Words by Christopher Brown, Robert Allen & Andre Merritt
Music by Brian Seals

Written by Chris Brown and Graffiti Artizts, 'Disturbia' was originally intended to be recorded for the re-release of Brown's album *Exclusive*. Brown decided that the song was better suited to a female singer and forwarded the track over to Rihanna, who released it on her own album re-release *Good Girl Gone Bad: Reloaded*.

Hints & Tips: Play through the left hand only from bar 9, until you are comfortable with the pattern of changes in the fingering.

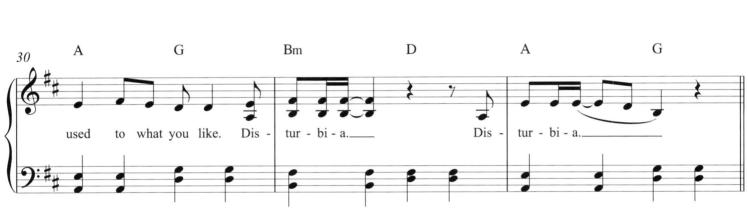

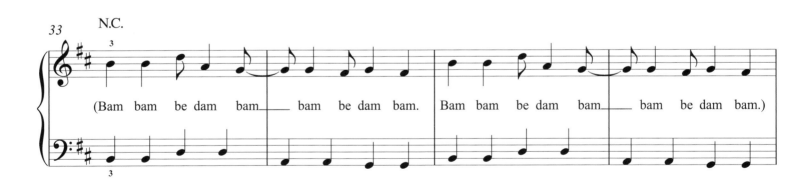

Don't Stop The Music

**Words & Music by Michael Jackson, Mikkel Eriksen,
Tor Erik Hermansen & Frankie Storm**

Using a line from Michael Jackson's 'Wanna Be Startin' Somethin'', this song is thought to be written about Rihanna's love affair with the music she likes. Filled with syncopation, samples and a number of rhythms and beats, the single is one of the most infectious dance floor fillers in Rihanna's back catalogue.

Hints & Tips: After the fairly steady rhythms all the way through, the melody becomes more syncopated from bar 26, so count carefully.

With a strong dance beat (♩ = 120)

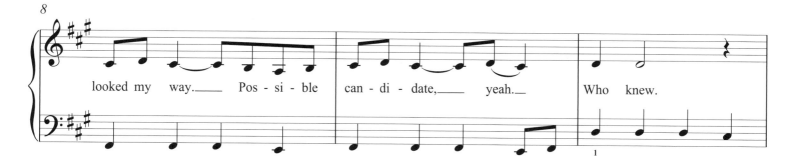

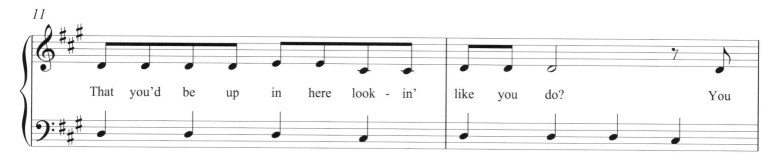

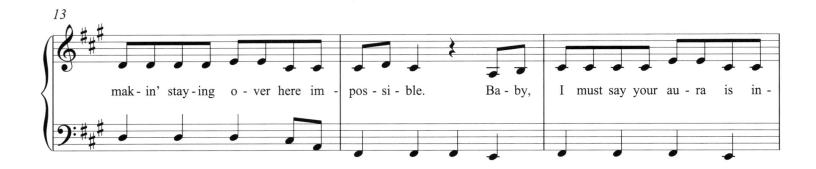

makin' stay-ing o-ver here im-pos-si-ble. Ba-by, I must say your au-ra is in-

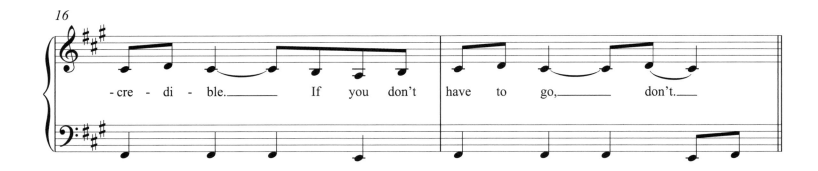

-cre-di-ble.____ If you don't have to go,____ don't.____

D

Do you know what you start-ed? I just came here to par-ty. But now we're rock-in' on the

F#m

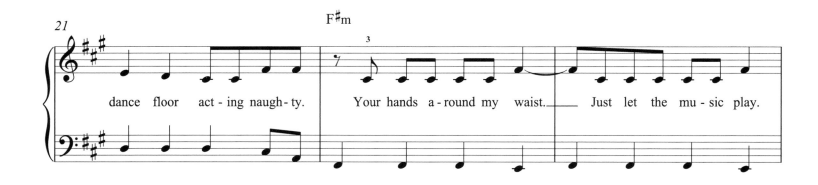

dance floor act-ing naugh-ty. Your hands a-round my waist.____ Just let the mu-sic play.

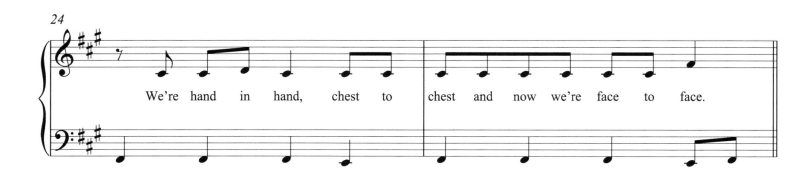

We're hand in hand, chest to chest and now we're face to face.

I wan - na take you___ a - way. Let's es - cape in - to the mu - sic.___ D. J. let___ it

play. I just can't re - fuse it. Like the way you do this. Keep on rock - in' to it. Please don't stop the,

please don't stop the mu - sic. I wan - na take you___ a - way. Let's es - cape in - to the

mu - sic.___ D. J. let___ it play. I just can't re - fuse it. Like the way you do this. Keep on rock - in'

to it. Please don't stop the, please don't stop the, please don't stop the mu - sic.

If I Never See Your Face Again

Words & Music by Adam Levine & James Valentine

This synth-heavy song by American pop rock band Maroon 5 features Rihanna dueting with lead singer Adam Levine. Rihanna was pleased to be asked to work with the group, stating that they were one of her favourite bands. It was featured on the re-release of her album *Good Girl Gone Bad*.

Hints & Tips: The chords at the end of bars 2, 4 and 6 are dissonant. This means that it sounds like the notes are clashing! Be confident when playing these chords.

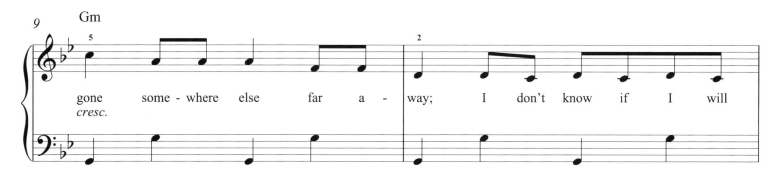

find you, find you, find you. But you feel my breath on your

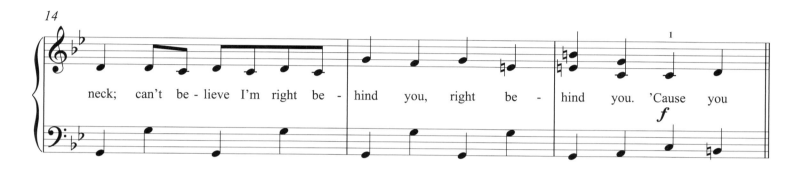

neck; can't be - lieve I'm right be - hind you, right be - hind you. 'Cause you

keep me com - ing back for more and I feel a lit - tle bet - ter than I

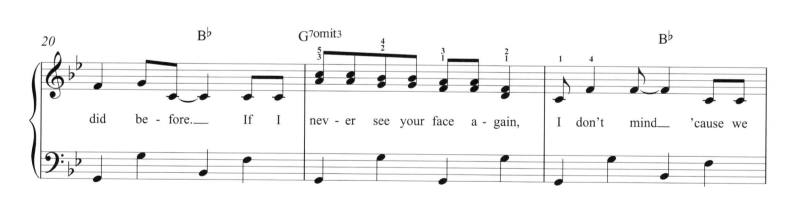

did be - fore. If I nev - er see your face a - gain, I don't mind 'cause we

got much fur - ther than I thought we'd get to - night.

Love The Way You Lie, Part II

Words & Music by Marshall Mathers, Holly Brook & Grant Alexander

Featuring vocals from multi-platinum-selling hip-hop artist Eminem, 'Love The Way You Lie, Pt. II' is an emotional track. A controversial hit due to its subject material, the song is a sequel to Eminem's 2010 hit 'Love The Way You Lie', which Rihanna famously featured on.

Hints & Tips: Play this song steady and soft, bringing out the melody.

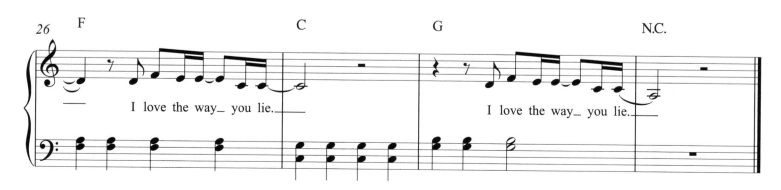

Russian Roulette

Words & Music by Shaffer Smith & Charles Harmon

The music video to this features Rihanna playing the deadly game referenced in the song's title. Released in 2009 as the lead single to her fourth studio album *Rated R*, speculation around the track's imagery and lyrics led many to believe it was a musical statement about the breakdown of her relationship with Chris Brown.

Hints & Tips: Make sure you hold down the lower note of the left hand for the full count of the bar, while the quavers on top are moving.

Princess Of China

**Words & Music by Chris Martin, Guy Berryman, Jon Buckland,
Will Champion & Brian Eno**

Coldplay frontman Chris Martin apparently had Rihanna in mind from the start for 'Princess Of China', which was written from a female point of view. After charting at number 33 on the UK Singles Chart upon its initial release in November 2011, the song dropped out of the charts before re-entering and clawing its way to the number 4 spot.

Hints & Tips: The phrases with the word 'Oh' held underneath should be played very smoothly, as in the song they are meant to be sung in one breath.

Stay

Words & Music by Justin Parker & Mikky Ekko

This song feels stripped down and intimate compared to Rihanna's more electronic, heavily produced hits. The song's lyrical themes of wanting or needing to hold onto someone are emphasised by the lack of resolution in the piano's harmonic progression. Throughout the first few choruses and verses in the song the chord progression returns time and time again to A minor, as if clinging onto the chord and feeling.

Hints & Tips: Keep the crotchet accompaniment steady and light in the left hand to let the tune really come through.

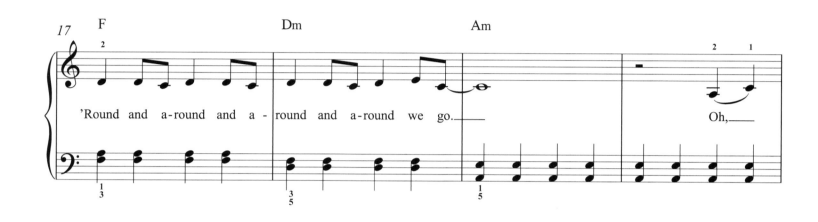

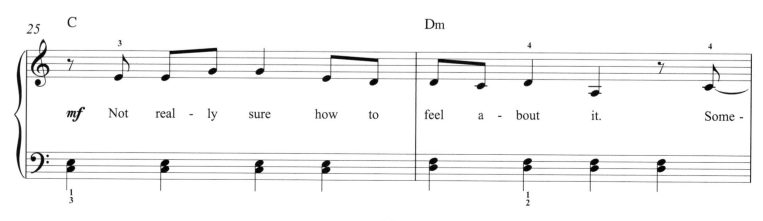

-thing in the way you move_____ makes_____ me feel like I can't

live with-out you. Yeah, it_____ takes me all the way. I want you to stay._

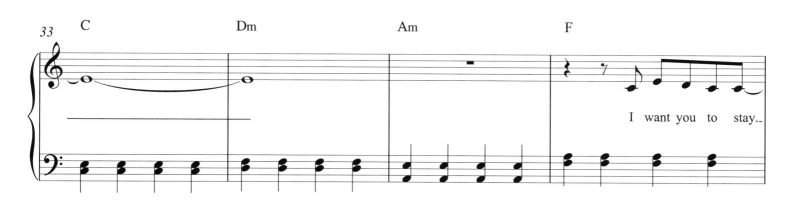

I want you to stay._

Ooh._____ _mp_

Take A Bow

Words & Music by Mikkel Eriksen, Tor Erik Hermansen & Shaffer Smith

Certified double platinum by the Recording Industry Association of America, 'Take A Bow' is one of Rihanna's biggest singles to date. With its harmonised backing vocals, piano accompaniment and kick drum, hand clap percussion, the song features many of the hallmarks of a modern R&B pop hit.

Hints & Tips: The right hand part in bars 9 and 11 requires the third finger to cross over the thumb. Move the third finger as you have finished playing the F so it is positioned ready to play the C when required, rather than leaving the movement to the last minute. Do the same with the thumb.

Te Amo

**Words & Music by Tor Erik Hermansen, Mikkel S. Eriksen,
Robyn Fenty & James Fauntlleroy II**

'Te Amo' means "I love you" in Spanish, and the track features many elements of Latin American music including rhythmic drum accompaniment and classical guitar strumming. Praised for its more organic sound compared to Rihanna's other more synth based hits, the song was an international hit.

Hints & Tips: This is quite a fast song with some tricky rhythms, so play through slowly then build up speed.

Take Care

Words & Music by Brook Benton, Wally Gold, Herb Wiener, James Smith, Romy Madley Croft, Aubrey Graham, Noah Shebib, John Gluck Jr., Seymour Sy Gottlieb & Anthony Palman

Rihanna provided the guest vocals to Drake's 'Take Care' released in 2012, scoring another top ten hit in a number of countries including the USA, UK and Australia alongside the Canadian rapper. The song samples elements from a remix of Gil Scott-Heron's 'I'll Take Care Of You'.

Hints & Tips: The chords in the left hand may seem tricky at first, but have a look and you'll notice the pattern is repeated all the way through. Once you've got the hang of it, it will seem easier to play.

Umbrella

**Words & Music by Christopher Stewart, Terius Nash,
Shawn Carter & Thaddis Harrell**

Originally written for Britney Spears, Rihanna was offered 'Umbrella' after Britney's label rejected it. Arguably it is the song that cemented Rihanna's status as a global pop mega star, topping the charts in the USA, UK, Canada, Germany, Australia, Ireland, Sweden and Switzerland as the lead single to her third album *Good Girl Gone Bad*.

Hints & Tips: Although this piece is fairly straightforward, do practise it slowly at first, ensuring that the notes in the right and left hand sound at exactly the same time when they are supposed to.

need me there; with you I'll al-ways share. Be - cause,

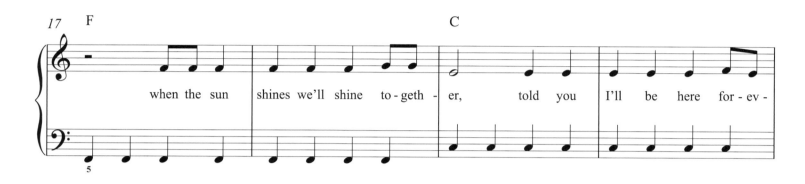

when the sun shines we'll shine to - geth - er, told you I'll be here for - ev -

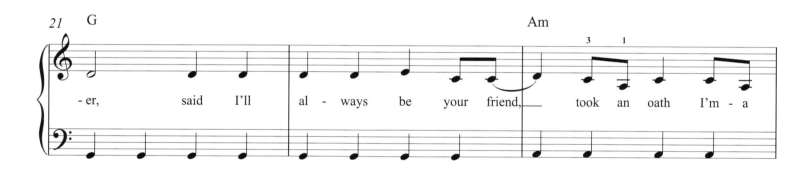

- er, said I'll al - ways be your friend,___ took an oath I'm - a

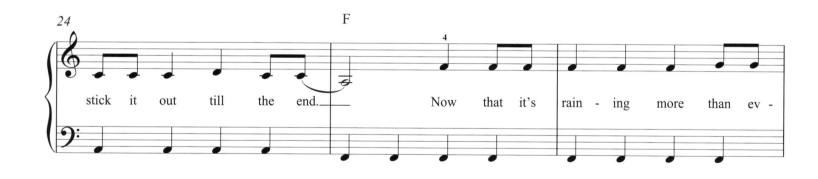

stick it out till the end.___ Now that it's rain - ing more than ev -

- er know that we'll still have each oth - er. You can stand

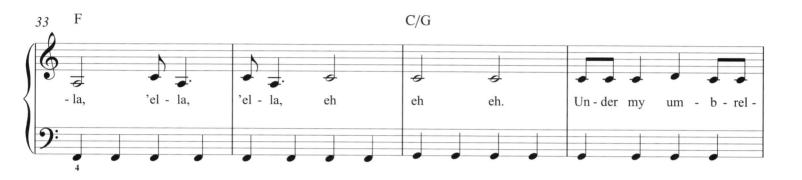

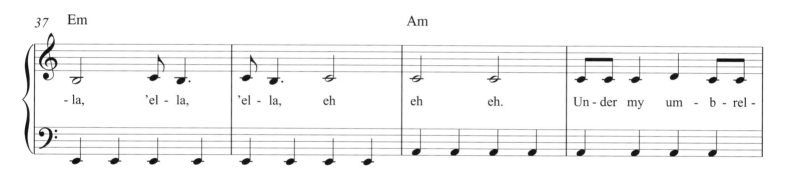

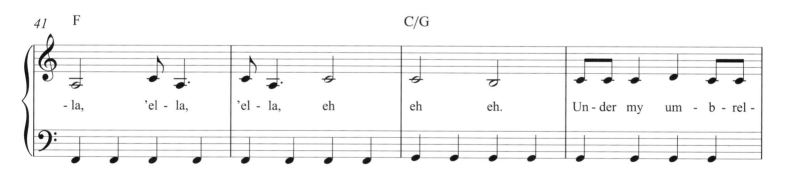

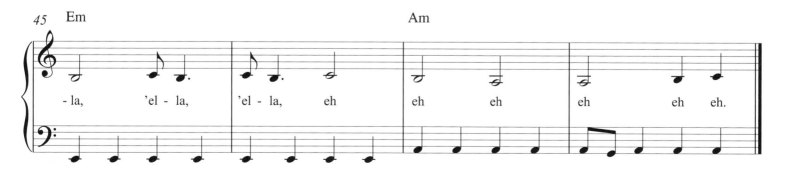

You Da One

**Words & Music by Lukasz Gottwald, Robyn Fenty,
Ester Dean, Henry Russell Walter & John Graham Hill**

Incorporating influences taken from dubstep, dancehall, reggae and electro-pop styles, this is perhaps the quintessential Rihanna hit. Combining electronic textures and production, a Caribbean vibe throughout and another memorable chorus, its mix of different musical flavours translated into international chart success.

Hints & Tips: Look out for the long slurred passages, e.g. bars 3–4, and make sure you play them nice and smoothly.

Unfaithful

**Words & Music by Mikkel Eriksen, Tor Erik Hermansen
& Shaffer Smith**

Written about a woman who regrets cheating on her partner 'Unfaithful' was originally titled 'Murderer' – the
ultimate line of the song's chorus. Now a staple of Rihanna's live performances, the track has featured on the
set lists for her *Good Girl Gone Bad*, *Last Girl on Earth* and *Loud* tours.

Hints & Tips: The right hand and left hand play quavers at the same time, but while the left hand moves
around, the right hand stays on the same note. Practise these bits carefully.